Contents

- **UNIT 1** — **School Shapes** 4
- **UNIT 2** — **Amazing Hair** 6
- **UNIT 3** — **Fancy Hat** 8
- **UNIT 4** — **Mud Cakes!** 10
- **UNIT 5** — **The Bug Hotel** 12
- **UNIT 6** — **Sandy Landscape** 14
- **UNIT 7** — **Pancake Day** 16
- **UNIT 8** — **Swings and Slides** 18
- My Progress 20
- Cutouts C1
- Stickers S1

The Bebop Band

The Bebop Friends

UNIT 1 School Shapes

Lesson 1

🎧 Sing the song: *Let's Discover*. Look and say. Find and color.

Lesson 2

A

B

Look at the steps. Create and paint! **Use the stickers for project A. Do project A, B, or both!**

UNIT 2 — Amazing Hair

Lesson 1

🎧 Sing the song: *Let's Discover*. Look and say.

Lesson 2

 Complete the drawing. Match your drawing to the hair style. C1 Color the cutout picture and add hair. Sing the song: *Where's My Hair?*

UNIT 3 — Fancy Hat

Lesson 1

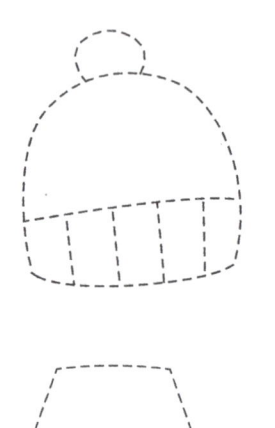
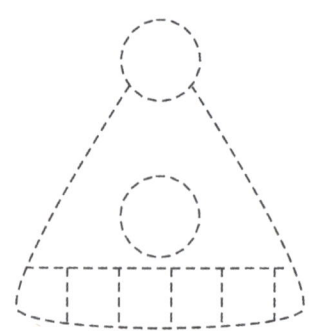

Sing the song: *Let's Discover.* Look and say. Trace the hats. Find the shape that matches the red hat. Color the hat red.

Lesson 2

Connect the hats to the Bebop friends. C3 **Make a collage hat using the cutout.**

UNIT 3

UNIT 4 — Mud Cakes!

Lesson 1

🎧 **Sing the song:** *Let's Discover.* **Look and say. Spread the correct color mud in the white box next to it.**

Lesson 2

1

2

3

4

Follow the steps. Make mud cakes for a birthday party! Draw a birthday cake on the plate.

UNIT 5 — The Bug Hotel

Lesson 1

🎧 **Sing the song:** *Let's Discover*. Look and say.

Unit 2   Cutout

C1

Unit 3   Cutout

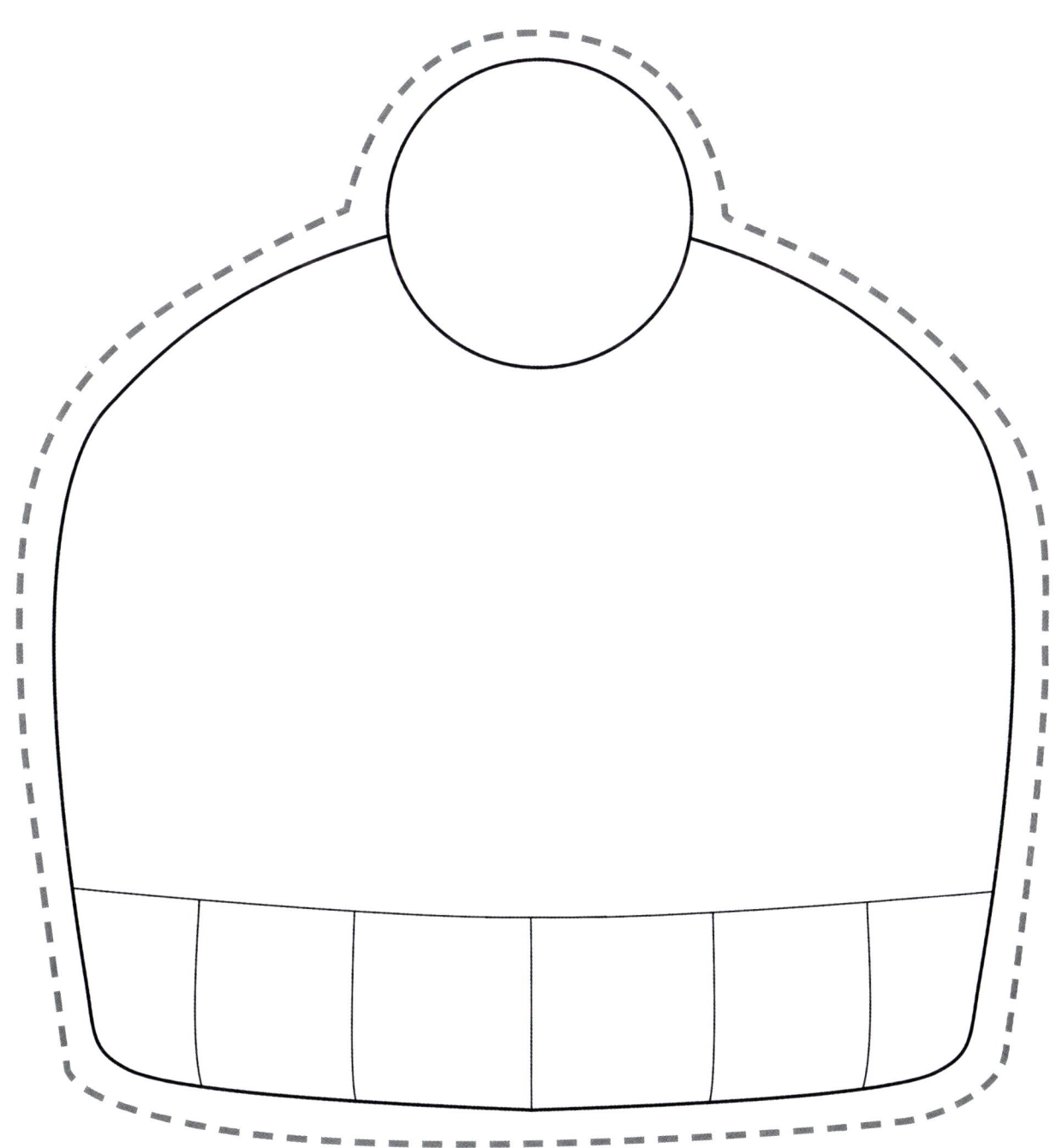

Unit 5   Cutouts

Unit 1 Stickers

Unit 6   Cutout

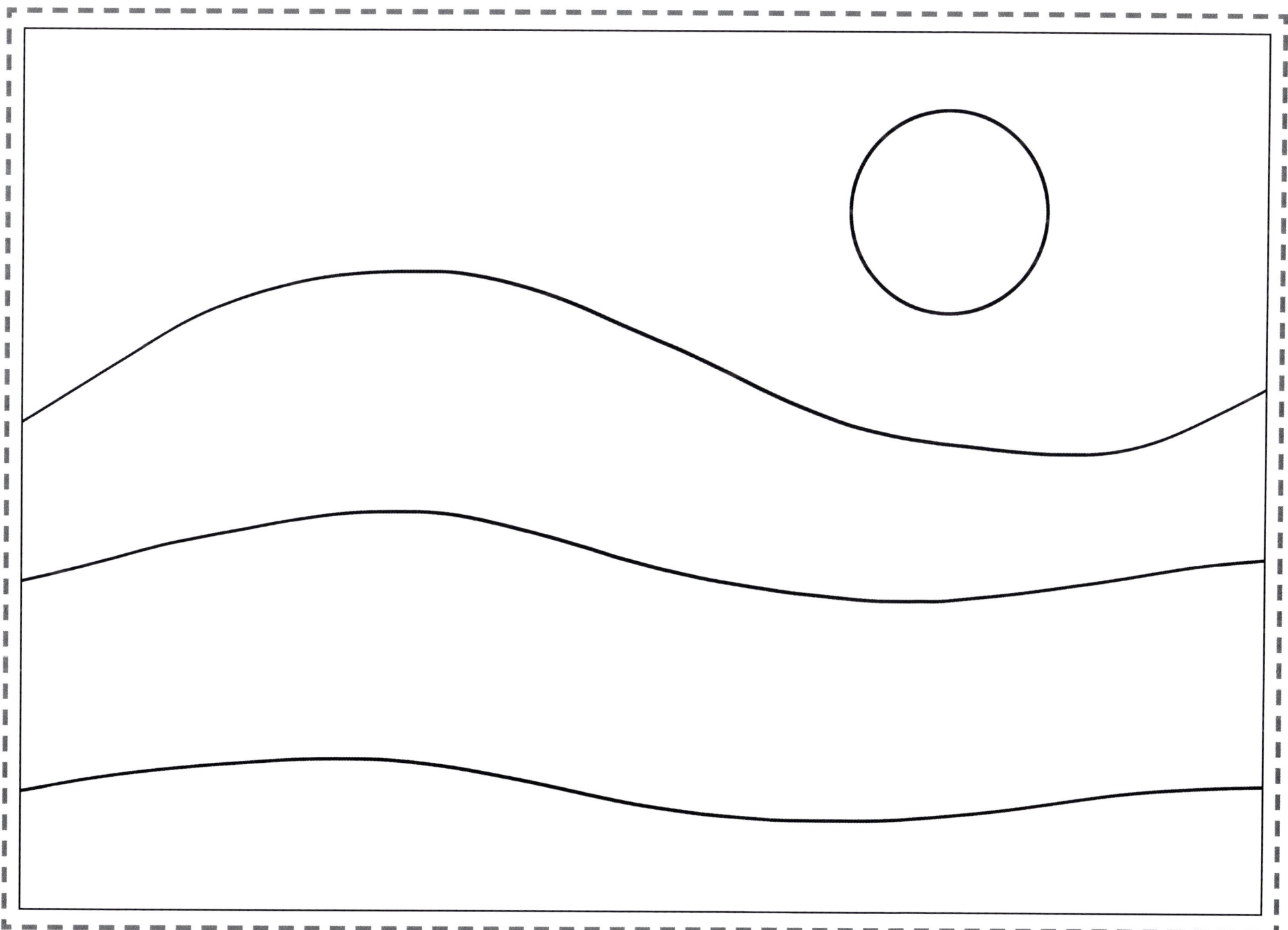

Unit 7 Cutout

Unit 8 Cutout

Lesson 2

Connect the correct animals to the bug hotel. C5 **Make a bug hotel using the cutouts.**

UNIT 6 · Sandy Landscape

Lesson 1

🎧 **Sing the song:** *Let's Discover*. Look and say.

Lesson 2

1

2

3

4

Follow the steps to make sand paintings. Paint the sand landscape cutout.

UNIT 7 · Pancake Day

Lesson 1

🎧 Sing the song: *Let's Discover*. Look and say.

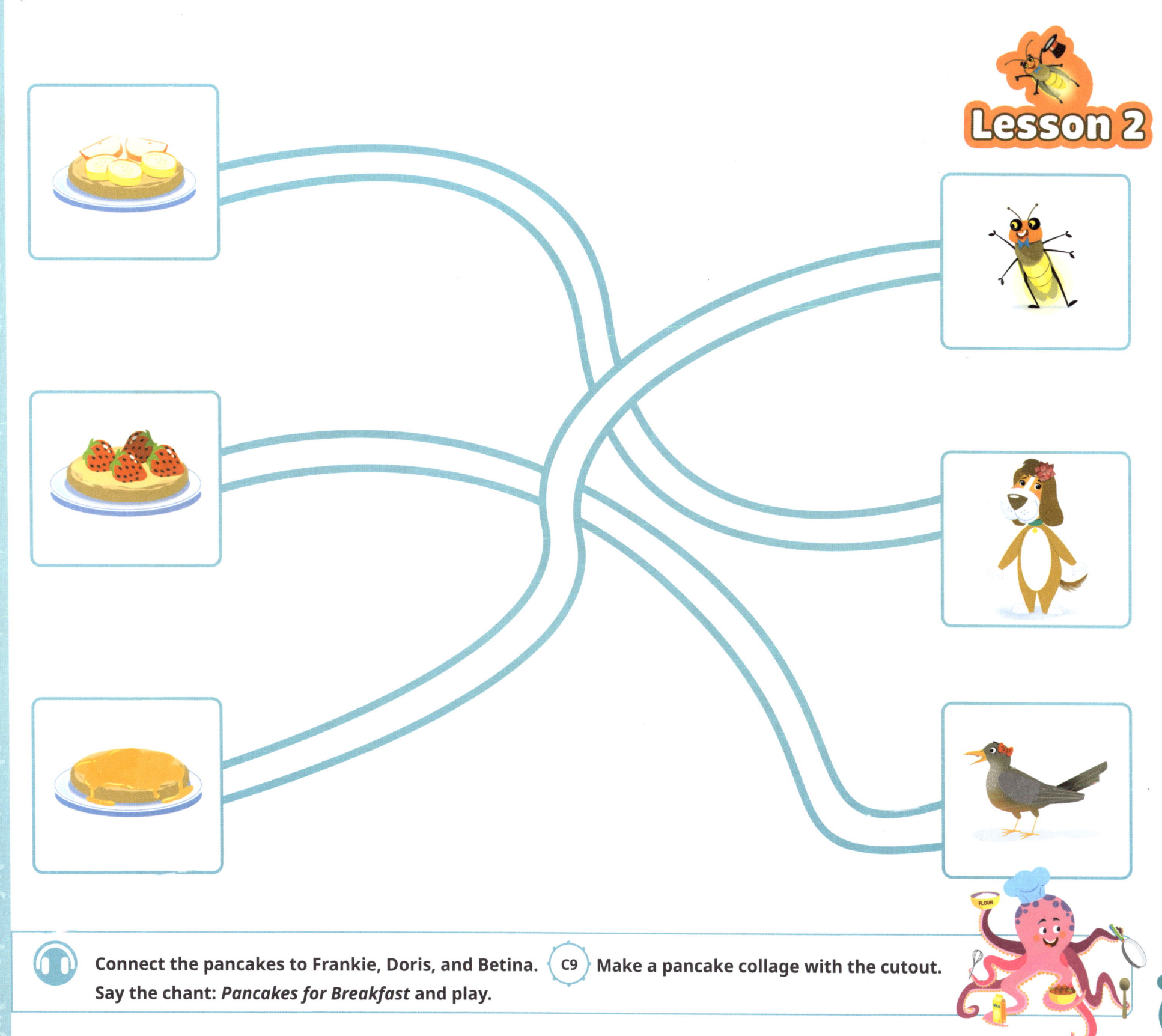

Connect the pancakes to Frankie, Doris, and Betina. Say the chant: *Pancakes for Breakfast* and play. C9 Make a pancake collage with the cutout.

UNIT 8 Swings and Slides

Lesson 1

🎧 Sing the song: *Let's Discover*. Look and say.

Lesson 2

  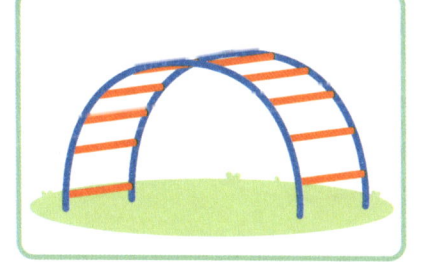 

Find and circle the swings with red and slides with purple. Paint the cutout park.

UNIT 8

My Progress

Color the number after you complete the unit.

Macmillan Education Limited
4 Crinan Street
London N1 9XW

Companies and representatives throughout the world

Bebop and Friends Level 2 Arts Book ISBN 978-1-035-10935-7
Bebop and Friends Level 2 Arts Book with Arts eBook Pack ISBN 978-1-035-10936-4

Text, design, and illustration © Macmillan Education Limited 2022
Written by Lucy Crichton

The author has asserted their right to be identified as the author of this work in accordance with the Copyright, Designs and Patents Act 1988.

This edition published 2022
First edition entitled "Bebop" published 2014 by Macmillan Education Limited

All rights reserved. No part of this publication may be reproduced, stored in a retrieval system, or transmitted in any form or by any means, electronic, mechanical, photocopying, recording, or otherwise, without the prior written permission of the publishers.

Design by Macmillan Education Ltd, with contributions by Design Divertido
Page makeup by Figurattiva Editorial
Illustrated by Ilustra Cartoon, Michelle Todd (The Bright Agency) p. 2
Cover design by Macmillan Education Limited
Cover illustration by Ilustra Cartoon
Picture research by Marcia Sato

The publishers would like to thank Rich Rafterman, Argila, and Minke Edição e Produção Cultural.

The author and publishers would like to thank the following for permission to reproduce their photographs:

Public Domain p. 4, **Fábio Gomes Trindade** p. 6, **Munch Museum**, Oslo p. 8, **Alena Polyarush** p. 10, **Fundatia Stefan Câltia** p. 12, **Tracy Turner** p. 14, **Megan Coyle** p. 16, **Ivan Onnellinen** p. 18, **Getty Images**/ iStockphoto/Natalie Ruffing p.13, Getty Images/iStockphoto/daseaford p.13, Getty Images/iStockphoto/AlexStar p.13, Getty Images/iStockphoto/Larysa Pashkevich p.13, Getty Images/iStockphoto/HHelene p.13, Getty Images/iStockphoto/Andrew_Howe p.13, Getty Images/iStockphoto/Irina Vasilevskaia p.13, Getty Images/iStockphoto/Chorna Olena p. C11

These materials may contain links for third party websites. We have no control over, and are not responsible for, the contents of such third party websites. Please use care when accessing them.

The inclusion of any specific companies, commercial products, trade names or otherwise does not constitute or imply its endorsement or recommendation by Macmillan Education Limited.

Printed and bound in Uruguay

2022
1